FIND DEMI'S
SEA CREATURES

An Animal Game Book

For Dr. Arthur
Stanwood Pier
who saves people
and whales, etc.

Putnam & Grosset   New York

Copyright © 1991 by Demi. All rights reserved.
Published by The Putnam & Grosset Book Group, New York.
Published simultaneously in Canada. Printed in Singapore.
Library of Congress Catalog Card Number: 90-83239
ISBN 0-399-22112-3   A B C D E F G H I J

THERE'S MORE TO THIS PAGE ➡

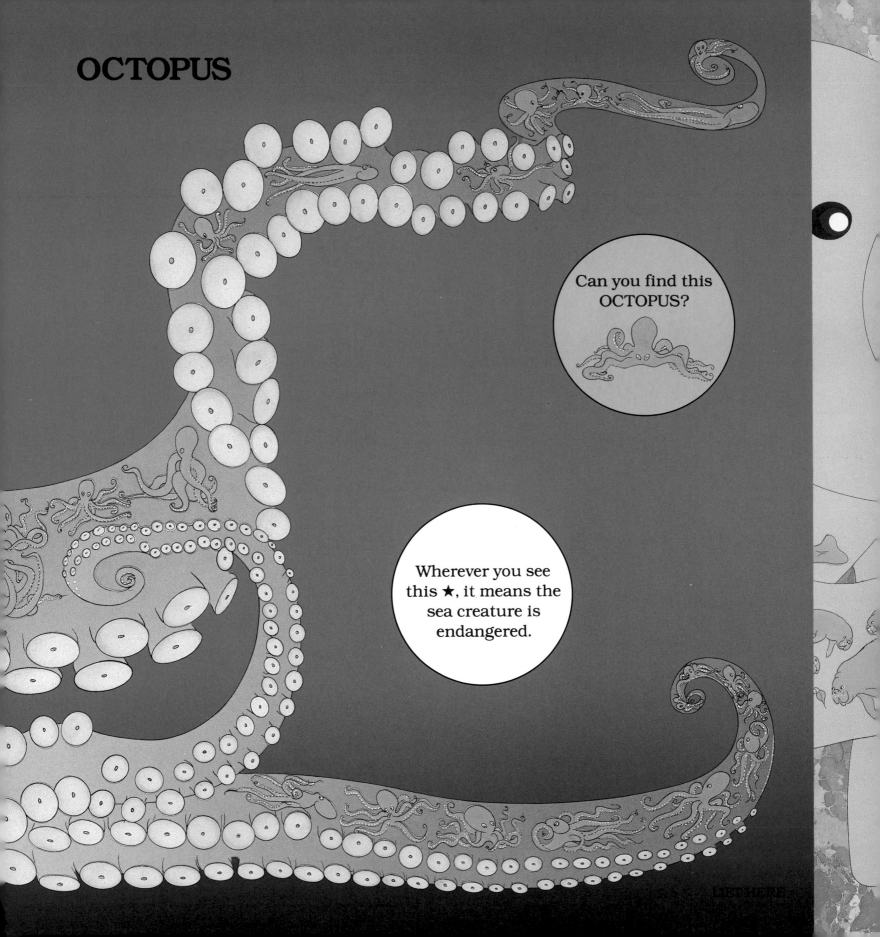

OCTOPUS

Can you find this OCTOPUS?

Wherever you see this ★, it means the sea creature is endangered.

MANATEES★

Can you find this
MANATEE?

FLYING FISH

Can you find this FLYING FISH?

CORAL FISHES

Can you find this
BUTTERFLY FISH?

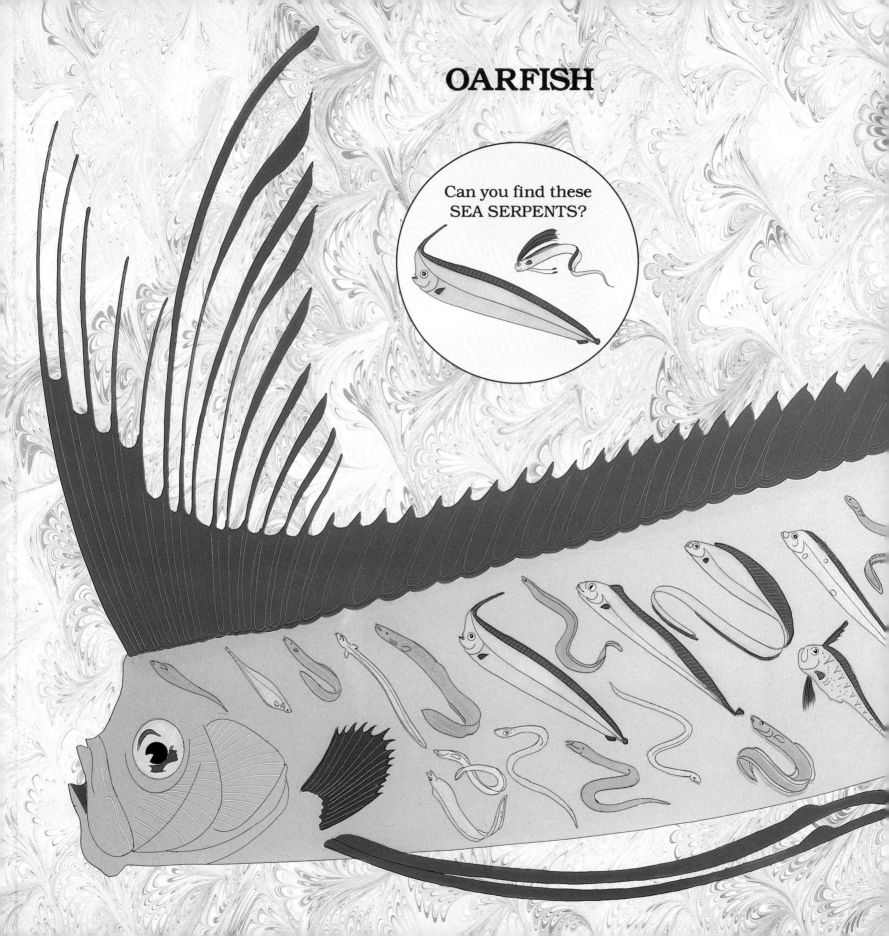

OARFISH

Can you find these
SEA SERPENTS?

THERE'S MORE TO THIS PAGE ➡

LIFT HERE

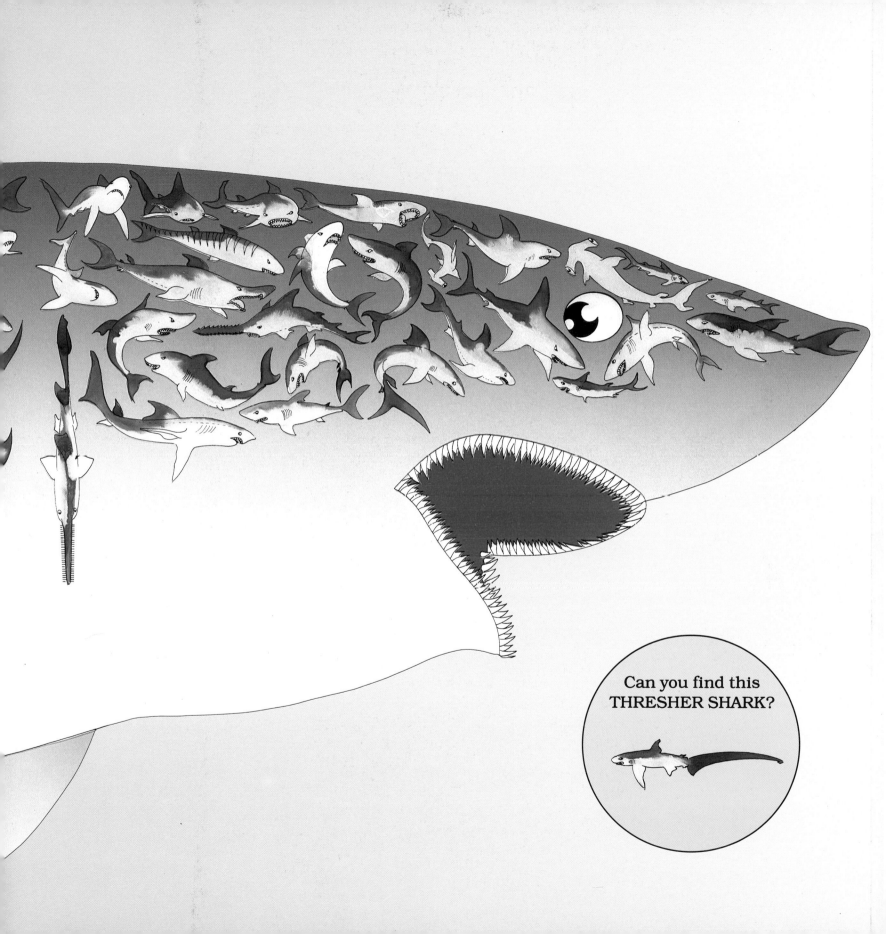

Can you find this
THRESHER SHARK?

ELECTRIC EEL

Can you find this
ELECTRIC
STARGAZER?

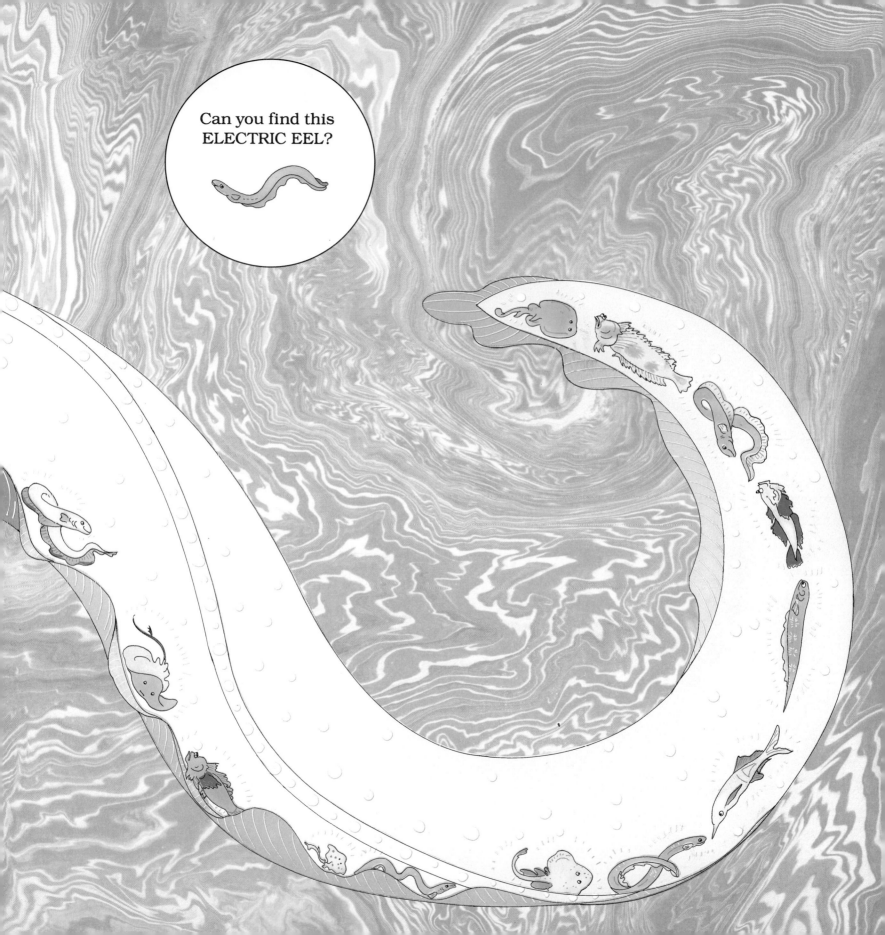

GIANT CLAM

Can you find this
GIANT CLAM?

SEA HORSES

Can you find these
SEA HORSES?

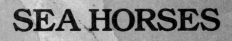

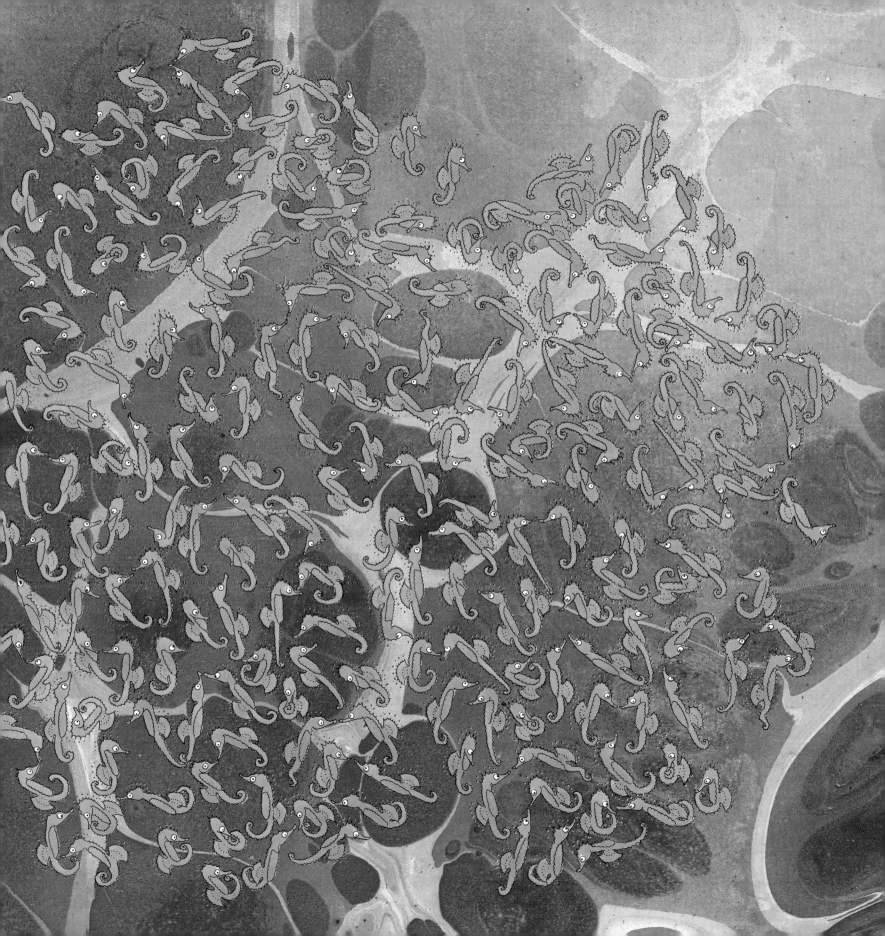

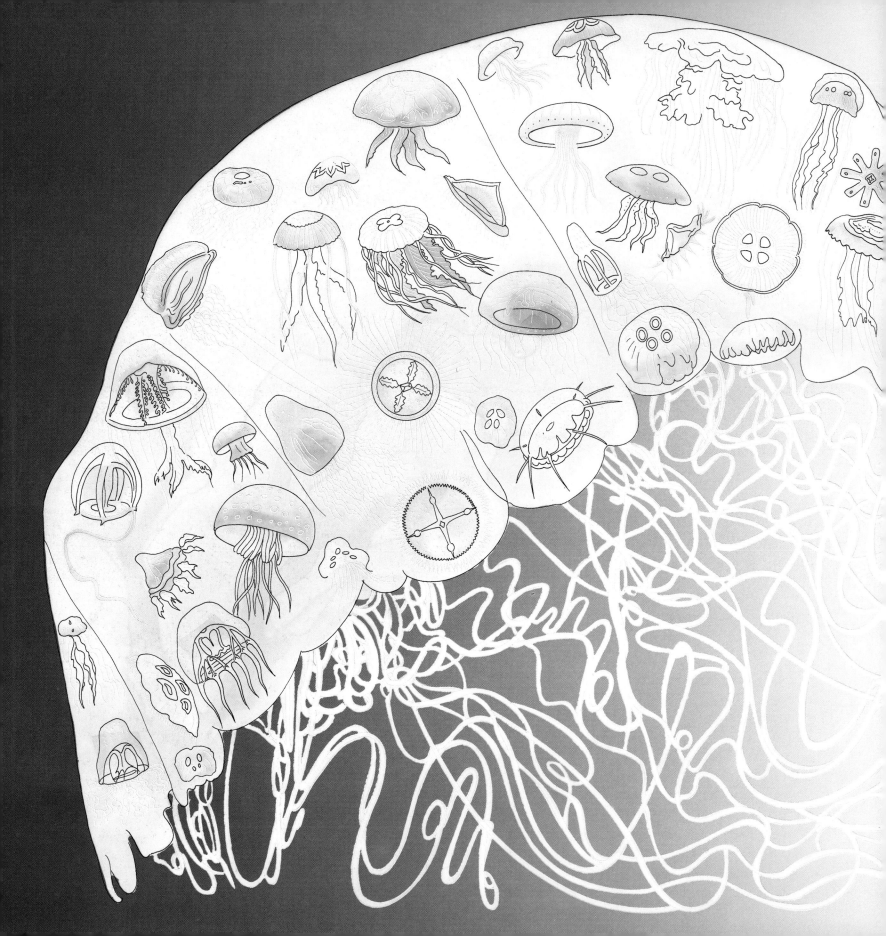

LION MANE JELLYFISH

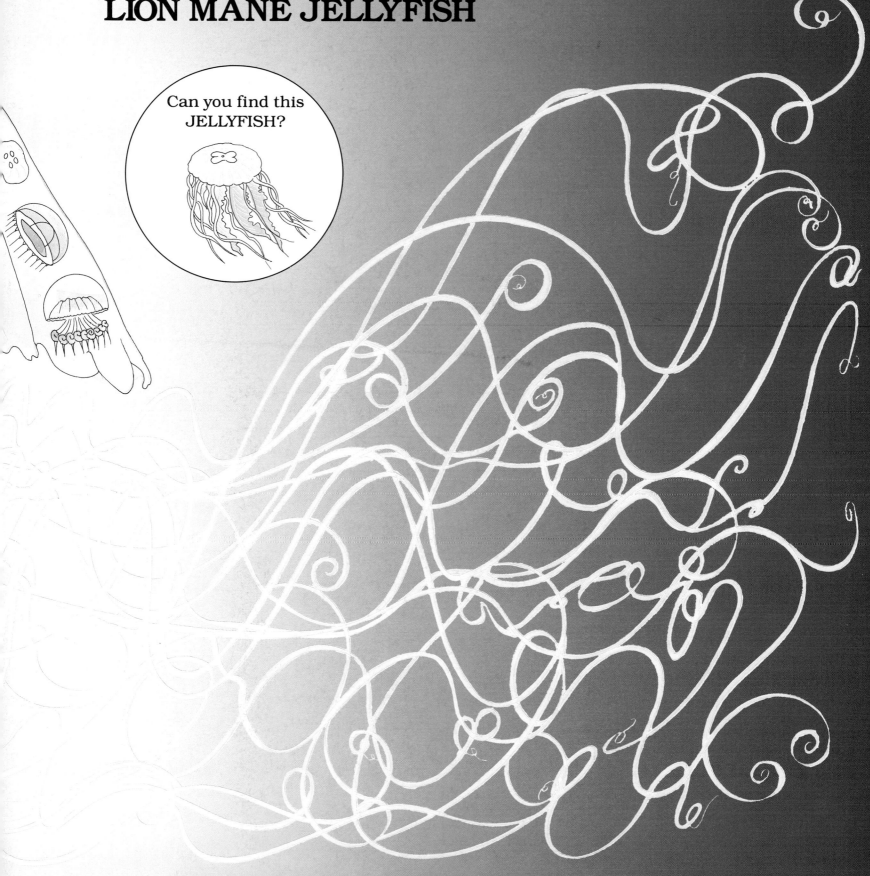

Can you find this
JELLYFISH?

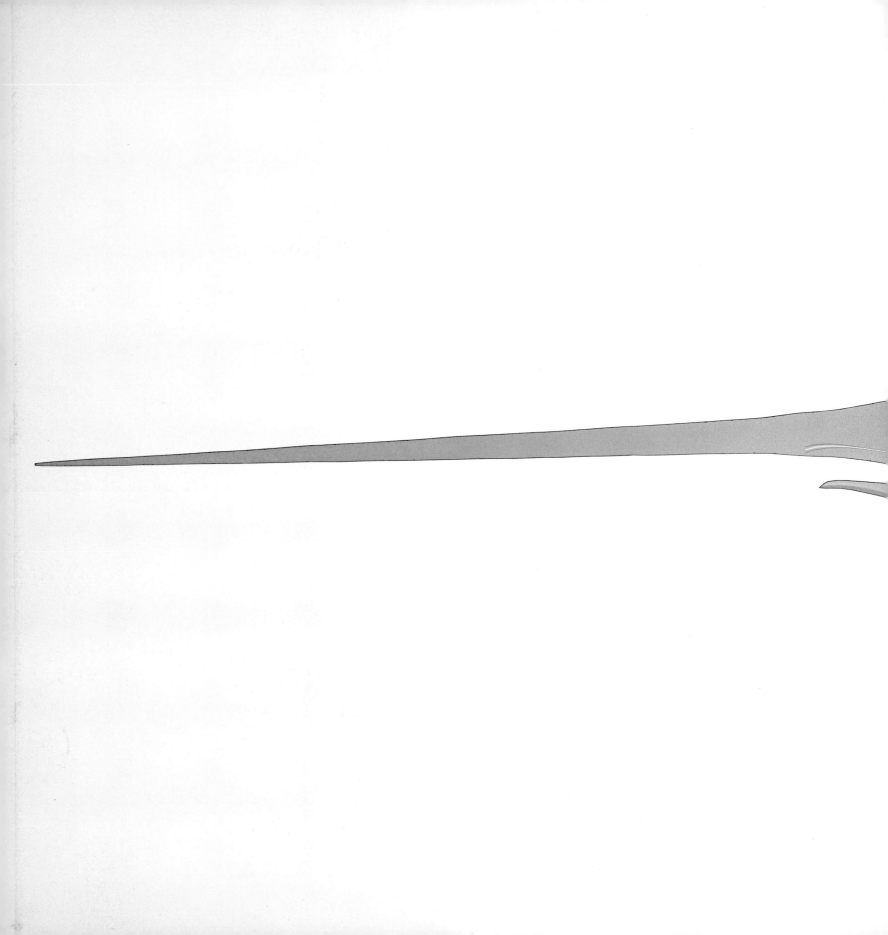

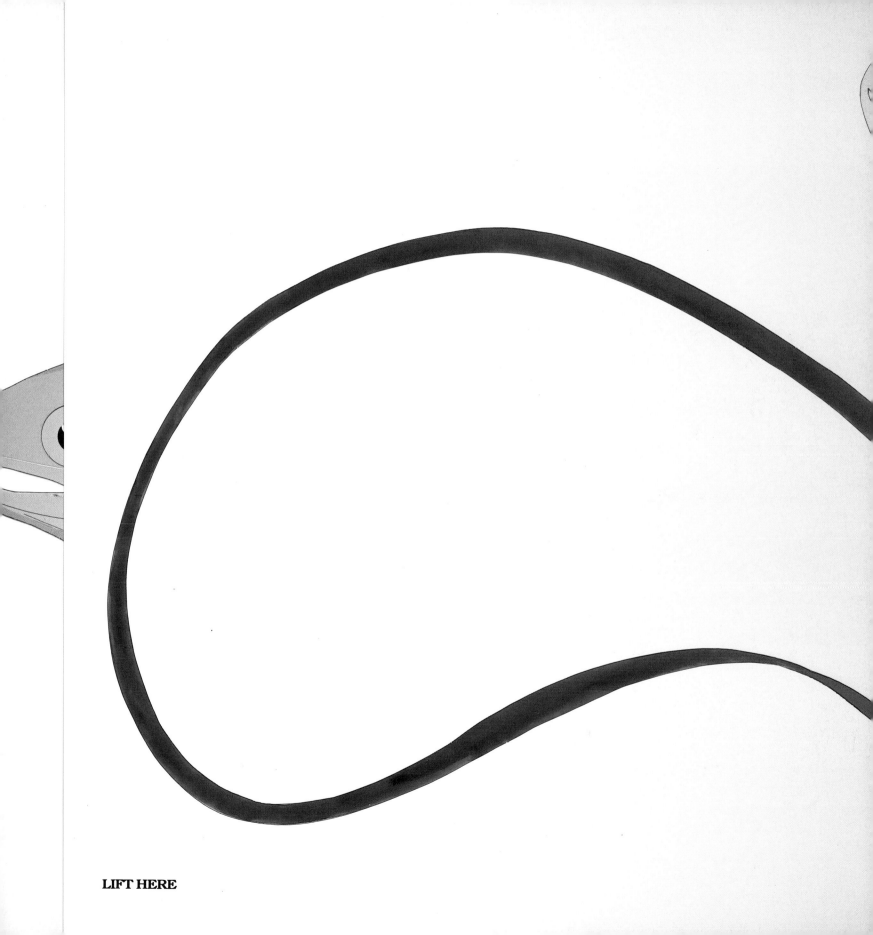

LIFT HERE

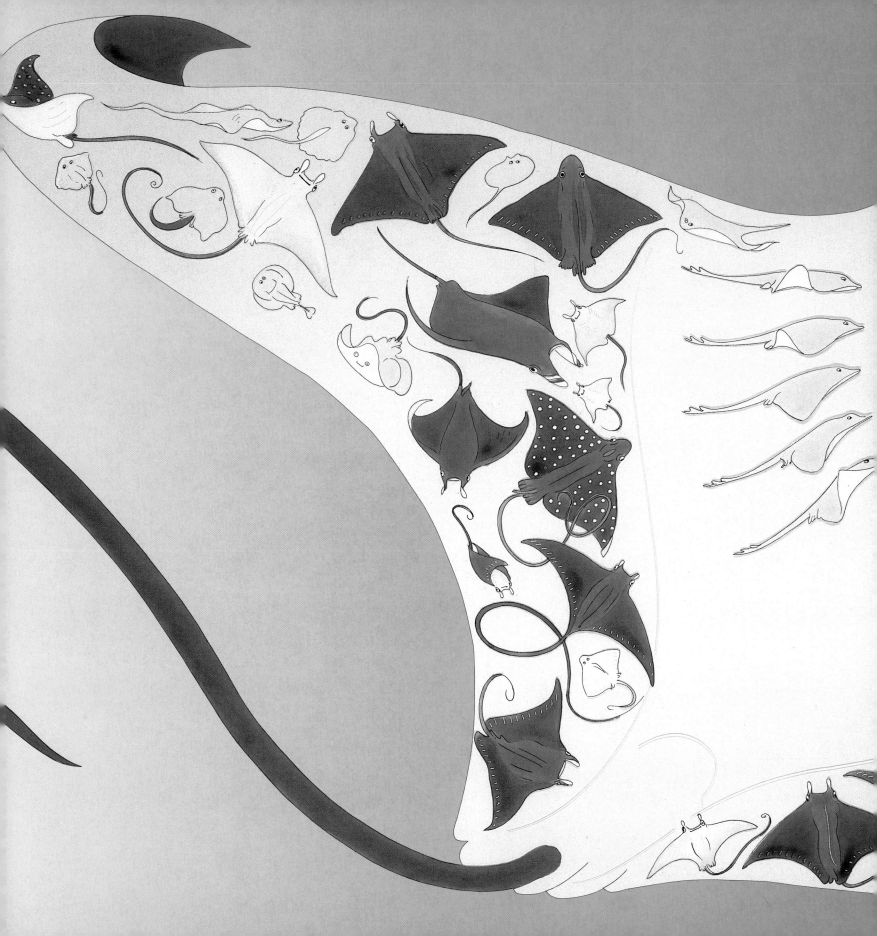

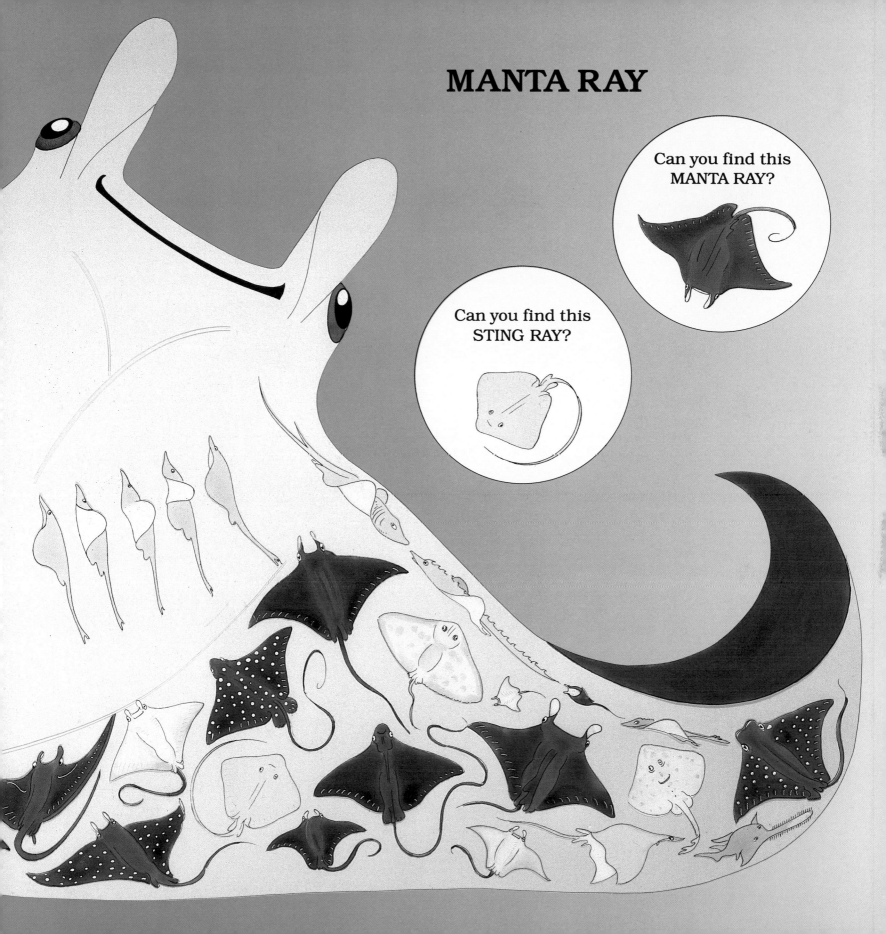

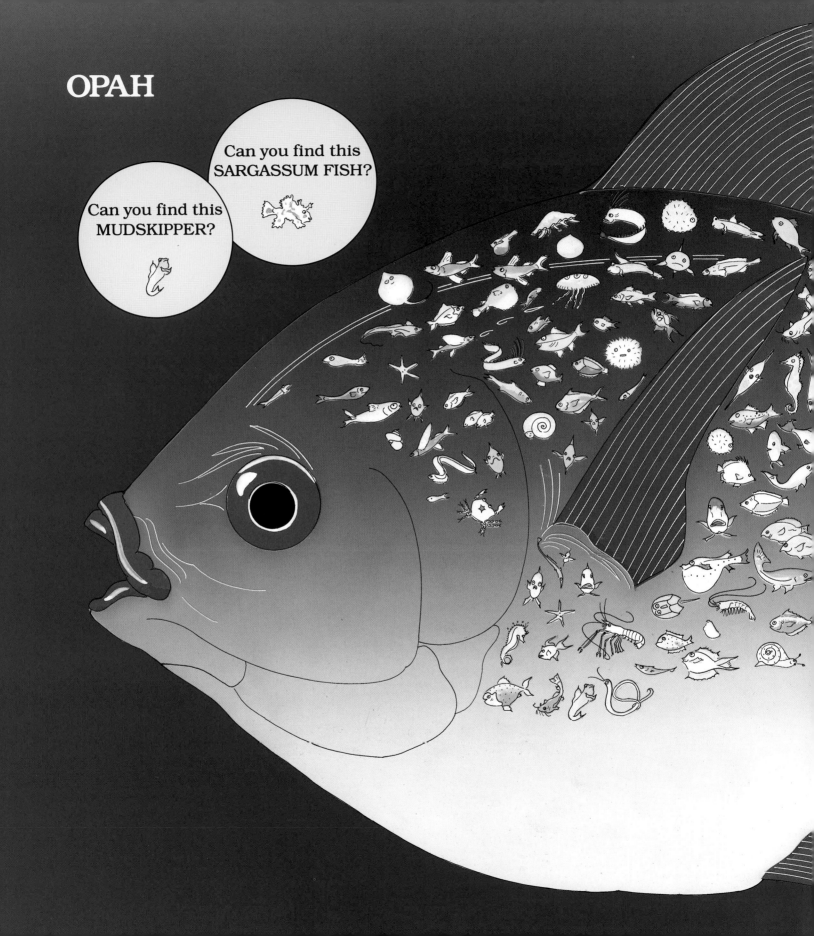

SEA TURTLE★

Can you find these
SEA TURTLES?

THERE'S MORE
TO THIS PAGE ➜

LIFT HERE

LIFT HERE

GIANT SQUID

Can you find this
GIANT SQUID?

Can you find this
HATCHET FISH?

DEEP SEA FISHES

Can you find this
VIPER FISH?

SEAWEED SEA STAR

Can you find this
SEA STAR?